Story by
PAUL TOBIN

Art and cover by
JACOB CHABOT

Colors by
MATTHEW J. RAINWATER

Letters by
STEVE DUTRO

DARK HORSE BOOKS

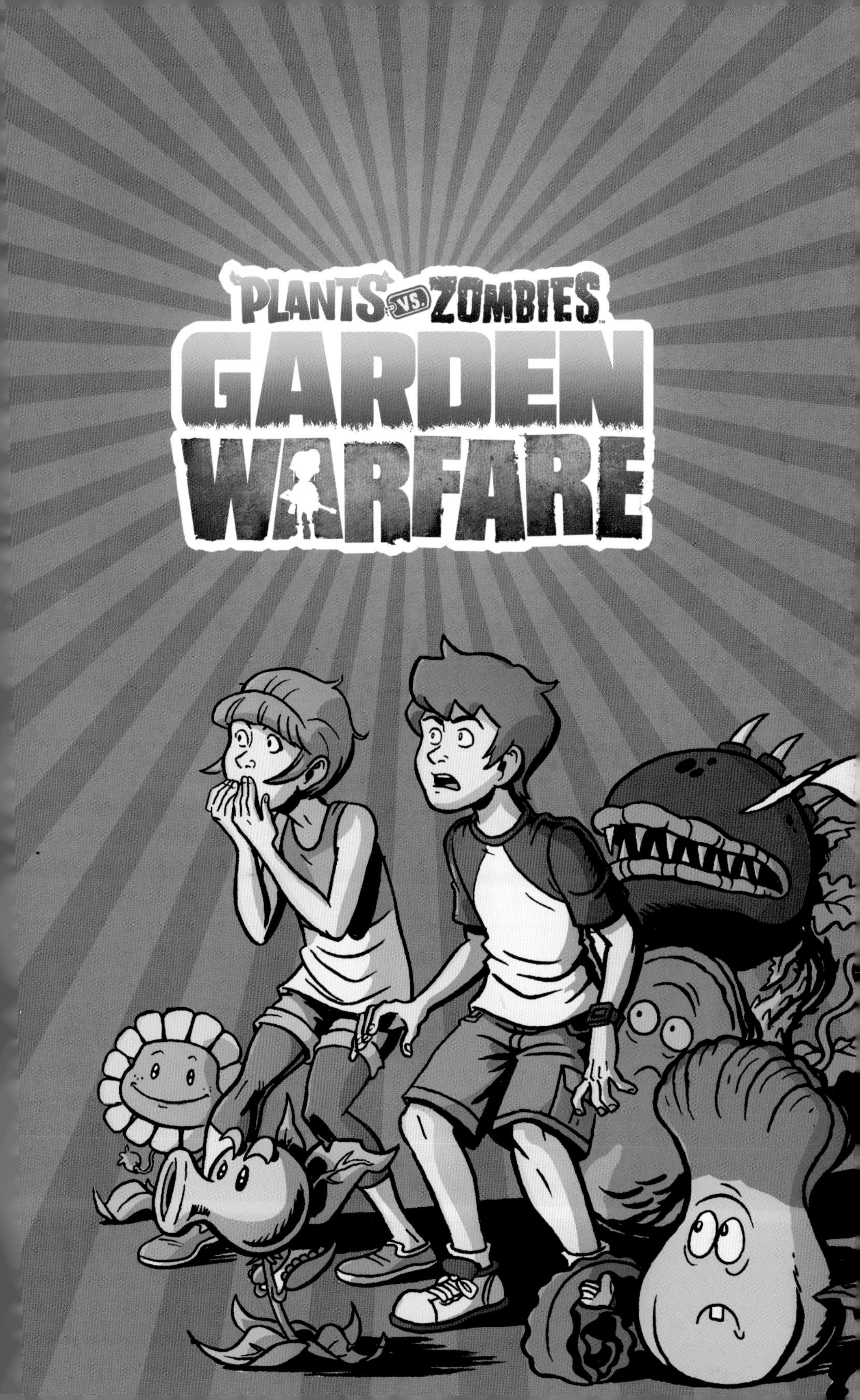
PLANTS VS. ZOMBIES
GARDEN
WARFARE

President and Publisher **MIKE RICHARDSON**
Editor **PHILIP R. SIMON**
Assistant Editor **ROXY POLK**
Designer **JIMMY PRESLER**
Digital Art Technician **CHRISTINA McKENZIE**

Special thanks to LEIGH BEACH, GARY CLAY,
SHANA DOERR, A.J. RATHBUN, KRISTEN STAR,
JEREMY VANHOOZER, and everyone at PopCap Games.

Scholastic edition: March 2016
ISBN 978-1-50670-101-1

10 9 8 7 6 5 4 3 2 1
Printed in China

DarkHorse.com | PopCap.com

▷ No plants were harmed in the making of this comic. Numerous zombies
and various zombie-focused mecha, however, definitely were.

This volume collects *Plants vs. Zombies: Garden Warfare* #1–#3, originally published by Dark Horse Comics in 2015. |
Published by Dark Horse Books, a division of Dark Horse Comics, Inc., 10956 SE Main Street, Milwaukie, OR 97222 |
International Licensing: (503) 905-2377 | To find a comics shop in your area, call the Comic Shop Locator Service toll-free
at 1-888-266-4226. | **PLANTS vs. ZOMBIES: GARDEN WARFARE.** Plants vs. Zombies © 2015, 2016 Electronic Arts Inc.

NEIL HANKERSON Executive Vice President **TOM WEDDLE** Chief Financial Officer **RANDY STRADLEY** Vice President of Publishing
MICHAEL MARTENS Vice President of Book Trade Sales **MATT PARKINSON** Vice President of Marketing **DAVID SCROGGY** Vice
President of Product Development **DALE LaFOUNTAIN** Vice President of Information Technology **CARA NIECE** Vice President of
Production and Scheduling **KEN LIZZI** General Counsel **DAVEY ESTRADA** Editorial Director **DAVE MARSHALL** Editor in Chief
SCOTT ALLIE Executive Senior Editor **CHRIS WARNER** Senior Books Editor **CARY GRAZZINI** Director of Print and Development

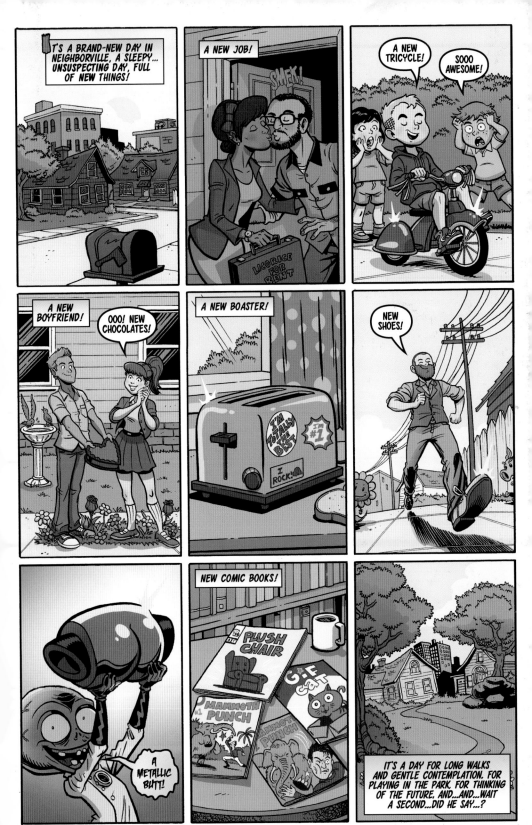

5

6

9

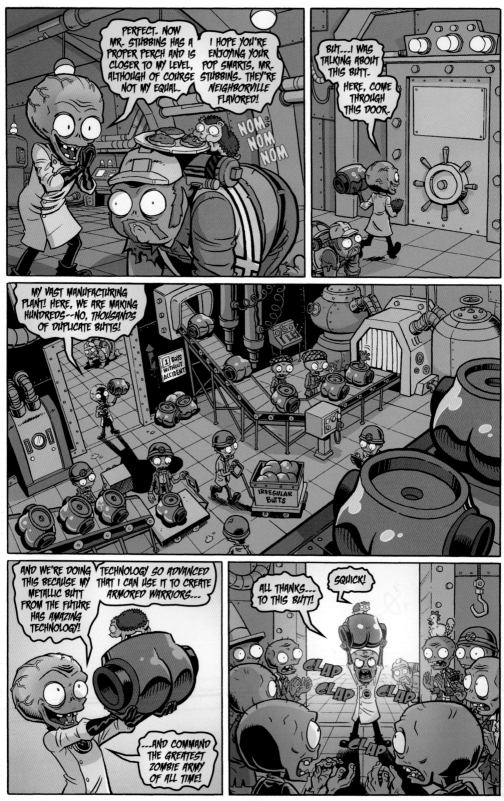

12

15

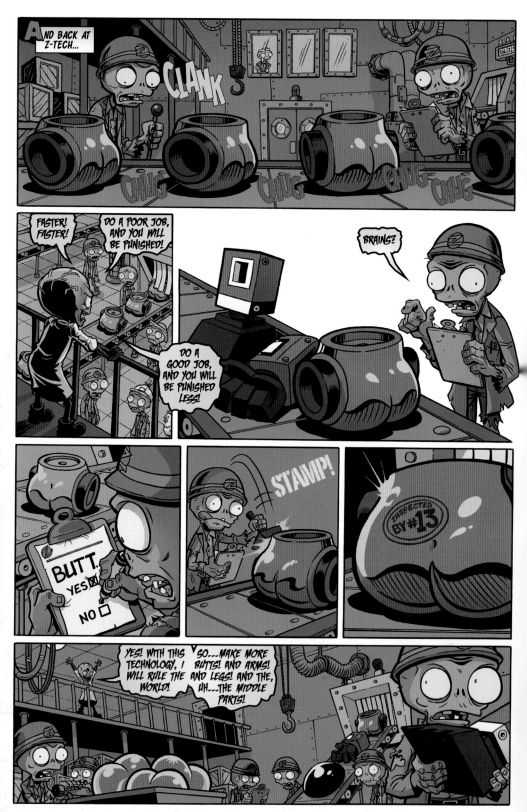

16

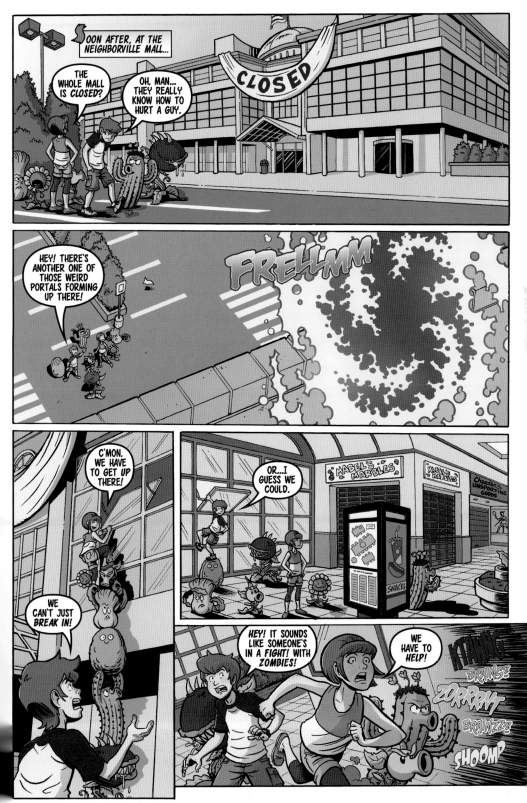

20

29

34

37

ELSEWHERE...

DAVE'S GARAGE

STRAP!

STRIPE!

WHAT ARE YOU UP TO, UNCLE DAVE?

GRALICK FLORO PLORNK!

UHHH...

YOU'RE... PUTTING ON ARMOR?

WHAT DO YOU MEAN... YOU'RE PUTTING ON ARMOR?

TSSSSS

RIBI RIBI BLOOG.

42

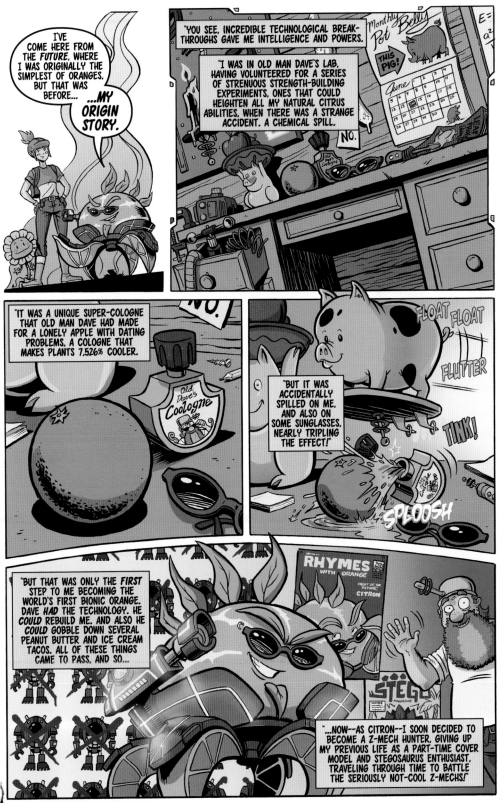

45

FIFTY YARDS AWAY...

IF YOU NEED TO DESTROY A Z-MECH...

...JUST ROLL UP LIKE *THIS*.

SCHWINNNG

AND BOMBAST THEM!

SPAAANK!

THAT'S HOW YOU PEEL AN IMP!

YEAH... THAT'S NOT GONNA WORK FOR ME.

I'LL STICK WITH *LITTLE MISS SUNSHINE*.

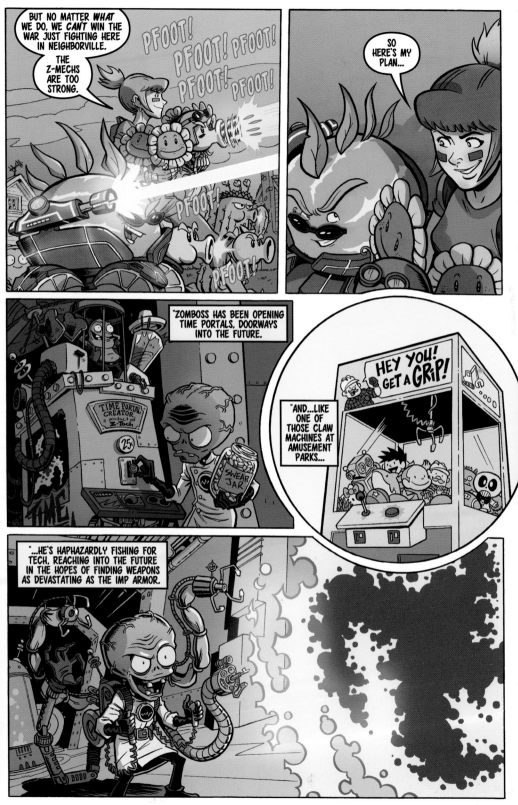

BUT NO MATTER *WHAT* WE DO, WE *CAN'T* WIN THE WAR JUST FIGHTING HERE IN NEIGHBORVILLE.

THE Z-MECHS ARE TOO STRONG.

PFOOT! PFOOT! PFOOT! PFOOT! PFOOT!

PFOOT!

PFOOT!

SO HERE'S MY PLAN...

"ZOMBOSS HAS BEEN OPENING TIME PORTALS, DOORWAYS INTO THE FUTURE.

TIME PORTAL CREATOR a product of Z-Tech

25¢

SWEAR JAR

HEY YOU! GET A GRIP!

"AND...LIKE ONE OF THOSE CLAW MACHINES AT AMUSEMENT PARKS...

"...HE'S HAPHAZARDLY FISHING FOR TECH, REACHING INTO THE FUTURE IN THE HOPES OF FINDING WEAPONS AS DEVASTATING AS THE IMP ARMOR.

51

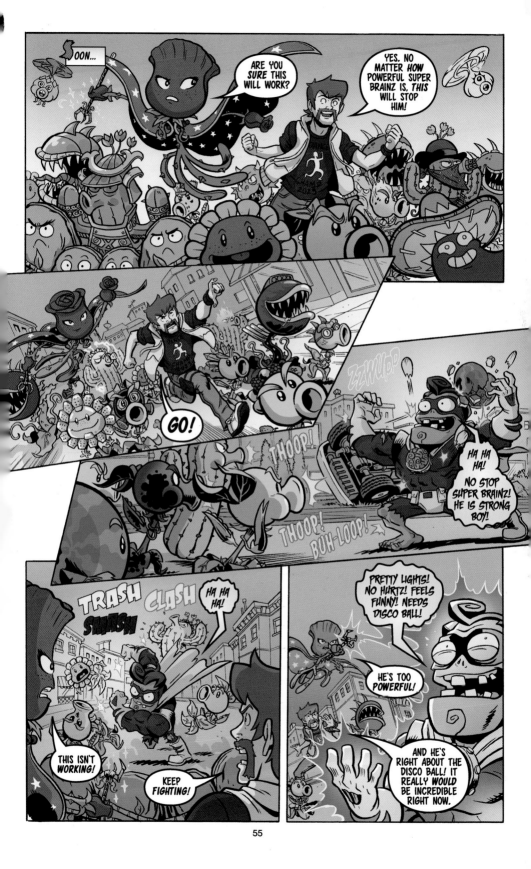

DOWNTOWN NEIGHBORVILLE...

ZOMBIE CONTROLLED
HUMAN CONTROLLED
MR. PIGG'S CONTROL (mean stray dog!)

MYSTERIOUS GNOMES ARE GATHERING!

TIME PORTALS?! BAH AND NO GOOD! LO-LO-LO!

THIS SHALL NOT STANDY-STAND! TRA-LA-LA!

ODDITIES ABOUND!

CAPTAIN DEAD-BEARD'S HERE, LADS.

YO-HO-HO AND A BARREL OF PARROTS!

HEROES ARISE!

COLONEL CORN!

THUPP

THUPP

SMACK SMACK

AND HEROES DESCEND!

59

64

HE FUTURE!

SMASH RHYMES WITH ORANGE!

SMASH!

SMASH DOES *NOT* RHYME WITH ORANGE!

SNACK

SHHH! THEY DON'T KNOW THAT!

ZEEE!!

ZEEE!!

ZEEE!!

WELL, WHAT I KNOW IS THAT ZOMBOSS *WON'T* STOP.

WE *HAVE* TO GET THAT E.M. PEACH READY!

AND FOR THAT...I NEED YOU TO KEEP THOSE Z-MECHS OFF MY BACK!

AND OFF MY FRONT. AND OFF MY FEET. AND OUT OF MY FACE. AND... DOWNWIND. BECAUSE THE IMPS DON'T *SMELL* VERY GOOD.

OH.

71

CREATOR BIOS

Paul Tobin

Jacob Chabot

Matthew J. Rainwater

Steve Dutro

PAUL TOBIN is a critically acclaimed freckled person who has a detailed plan for any actual zombie invasion, based on creating a vast perfume and cologne empire—both of which would be vitally important in a zombie-infested world. Paul was once informed he "walks funny, like, seriously," but has recovered from this childhood trauma to write hundreds of comics for Marvel, DC, Dark Horse, and many others, including such creator-owned titles as *Colder* and *Bandette*, as well as *Prepare to Die!*—his debut novel. His *Genius Factor* series of novels about a fifth-grade genius and his war against the Red Death Tea Society begins in March of 2016 from Bloomsbury Publishing. Despite his many writing accomplishments, Paul's greatest claim to fame is his ability to win water levels in *Plants vs. Zombies* without using any water plants.

JACOB CHABOT is a New York City–based cartoonist and illustrator. His credits include work for *SpongeBob Comics*, *Simpsons Comics*, Marvel Comics, *Hello Kitty*, and his own Eisner-nominated book *The Mighty Skullboy Army* (published by Dark Horse Comics). He also has almost all the achievements in *Plants vs. Zombies*

Garden Warfare, and if he could stop drawing for a minute, maybe he could finish them all!

Residing in the cool, damp forests of Portland, Oregon, **MATTHEW J. RAINWATER** is a freelance illustrator whose work has been featured in advertising, web design, and independent video games. On top of this, he also self-publishes several comic books, including *Trailer Park Warlock*, *Garage Raja*, and *The Feeling Is Multiplied*—all of which can be found at MattJRainwater.com. His favorite zombie-bashing strategy utilizes a line of Bonk Choys with a Wall-nut front guard and Threepeater covering fire.

STEVE DUTRO is a comic book letterer from northern California who can also drive a tractor. He graduated from the Kubert School and has been in the comics industry for decades, working for Dark Horse (*The Fifth Beatle*, *The Evil Dead*, *Eden*), Viz, Marvel, and DC. Steve's last encounter with zombies was playing zombie paintball in a walnut orchard on Halloween. He tried to play the *Plants vs. Zombies* video game once but experienced a full-on panic attack and resolved to stick with calmer games . . . like *Gears of War*.

MORE DARK HORSE ALL-AGES TITLES

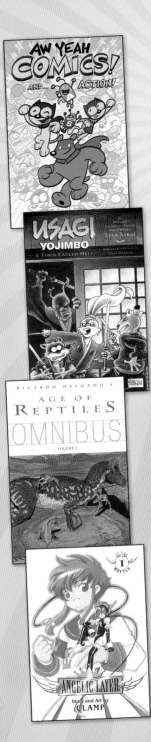

AW YEAH COMICS! AND . . . ACTION!

Cornelius and Alowicious are just your average comic book store employees, but when trouble strikes, they are . . . Action Cat and Adventure Bug! Join their epic all-ages adventures as they face off—with the help of Adorable Cat and Shelly Bug—against their archnemesis, Evil Cat, and his fiendish friends!

ISBN 978-1-61655-558-0 | $12.99

USAGI YOJIMBO

In his latest adventure, the rabbit *ronin* Usagi finds himself caught between competing gang lords fighting for control of a town called Hell, confronting a *nukekubi*—a flying cannibal head—and crossing paths with the demon Jei!

Volume 25: Fox Hunt
ISBN 978-1-59582-726-5 | $16.99

Volume 26: Traitors of the Earth | $16.99
ISBN 978-1-59582-910-8

Volume 27: A Town Called Hell | $16.99
ISBN 978-1-59582-970-2

AGE OF REPTILES OMNIBUS

When Ricardo Delgado first set his sights on creating comics, he crafted an epic tale about the most unlikely cast of characters: dinosaurs. Since that first Eisner-winning foray into the world of sequential art he has returned to his critically acclaimed *Age of Reptiles* again and again, each time crafting a captivating saga about his saurian subjects.

ISBN 978-1-59582-683-1 | $24.99

ANGELIC LAYER BOOK 1

Junior-high student Misaki Suzuhara just arrived in Tokyo to live with her TV-star aunt and attend the prestigious Eriol Academy. But what excites Misaki most is Angelic Layer—an arena game where you control a miniature robot fighter with your mind! Can Misaki's enthusiasm and skill take her to the top of the arena?

ISBN 978-1-61655-021-9 | $19.99